MANGA MATHS MYSTERIES

THE LOST KEY

A Mystery with Whole Numbers

by Melinda Thielbar
illustrated by Tintin Pantoja

Lerner

LERNER BOOKS
LONDON • NEW YORK • MINNEAPOLIS

What is a **whole number**? Whole numbers are the **counting numbers** and also **zero**: 0, 1, 2, 3, 4 and so on.

We use whole numbers every day. We use them to count, add, subtract, multiply and divide.

Story by Melinda Thielbar
Pencils and inks by Tintin Pantoja
Colouring by Hi-Fi Design
Lettering by Marshall Dillon

Copyright © 2010 by Lerner Publishing Group, Inc.

Graphic Universe™ is a trademark of Lerner Publishing Group, Inc.

First published in the United Kingdom in 2010 by
Lerner Books,
Dalton House,
60 Windsor Avenue,
London SW19 2RR

Website address: www.lernerbooks.co.uk

This edition was edited for UK publication in 2010

A CIP record for this book is available from the British Library

First published in the United States of America in 2010

Printed in China

5

11

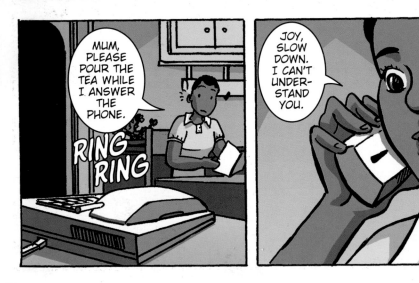

Top shelf

Middle shelf
22 total slots.
11 slots have one T-shirt in each. The rest have one pair of shorts in each.
22 − 11 = 11 slots have shorts.

Bottom shelf
1 football.

HERE IT IS!

LET'S SEE WHAT'S IN THE BAG, AND JOY CAN TELL US WHERE IT GOES ON THE SHELF.

WE HAVE SOME SKIPPING ROPES.

THE SKIPPING ROPES GO ON THE TOP SHELF.

1, 2, 3, 4, 5, 6, 7, 8, 9, 10, 11. THERE ARE 11 SLOTS.

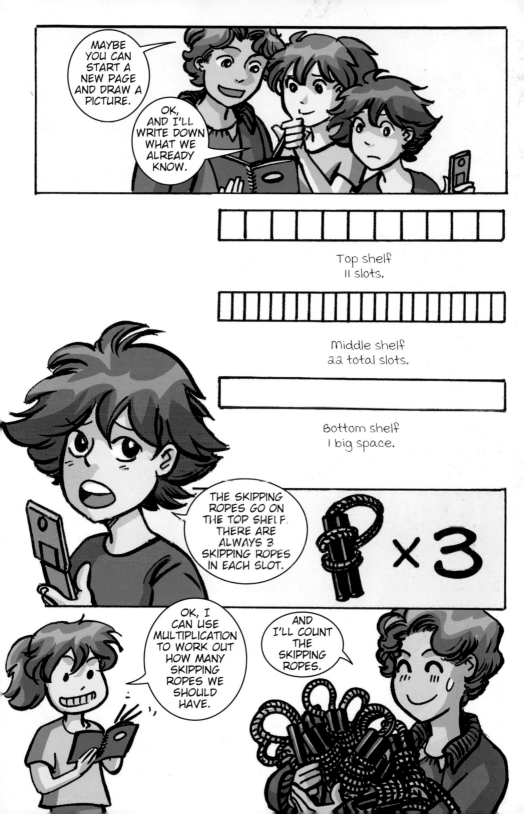

SOME OF THE DIRECTIONS ARE MISSING. DO YOU GUYS KNOW HOW TO GET TO THE FOOTBALL PITCH FROM HERE?

DRIVING DIRECTIONS FOR COLONIAL HEIGHTS FOOTBALL PITCH

It's only 9 blocks to the football pitch. Follow these easy directions.

1. Go 3 blocks South and tu

2. Go and turn

3. Go 3 more blocks and you are there.

NOT ME.

NO.

MAYBE WE CAN WORK OUT THE DIRECTIONS FROM WHAT'S HERE.

1. Go 3 blocks South and tu

2. Go and turn

SALE 50¢

3. Go 3 more b and you are th

THERE ARE 9 TOTAL BLOCKS, AND WE'RE MISSING THE PIECE IN THE MIDDLE. SO LET'S BREAK THE TRIP INTO 3 EQUAL PIECES. WE SHOULD DIVIDE 9 BY 3.

9 total blocks divided into 3 equal parts.

Each part of the trip is 9 ÷ 3 = 3 blocks long.

Top shelf
11 slots.
3 skipping ropes for each slot.
11 × 3 = 33 jump ropes.

Middle shelf
22 total slots.
1 focus mitt per slot.
22 × 1 = 22 total focus mitts.

Bottom shelf
1 big space.

Middle shelf
22 total slots.
1 focus mitt per slot.
22 × 1 = 22 total focus mitts.
2 mitts per pair.
22 ÷ 2 = 11 pairs of focus mitts.

Bottom shelf
1 big space.
1 helmet for each pair of focus mitts.
11 × 1 = 11 helmets.

44

CAN I HELP YOU CARRY THIS STUFF BACK TO THE KUNG FU SCHOOL?
...
!
SURE. COME ON.
SMILE!
WOW. I'M REALLY HUNGRY.
ME, TOO. YOU GUYS WANT TO COME TO MY HOUSE FOR DINNER?
STACY, YOU CAN COME TOO, IF YOU WANT.
NO THANKS. I HAVE A GAME TOMORROW.
?
3
THANKS FOR YOUR HELP. YOU KNOW, IF YOU EVER WANT TO LEARN KUNG FU--
I LIKE FOOTBALL, BUT KUNG FU LOOKS COOL TOO.

The Author

Melinda Thielbar is a teacher who has written maths courses for all ages, from kids to adults. In 2005 Melinda was awarded a VIGRE fellowship at North Carolina State University for PhD candidates "likely to make a strong contribution to education in mathematics." She lives in Raleigh, North Carolina, with her husband, author and video game programmer Richard Dansky, and their two cats.

The Artists

Tintin Pantoja was born in Manila in the Philippines. She received a degree in Illustration and Cartooning from the School of Visual Arts in New York City and was nominated for the Friends of Lulu "Best Newcomer" award. She was also a finalist in Tokyopop's Rising Stars of Manga 5. Her past books include a graphic novel version for kids of Shakespeare's play *Hamlet*.

Yuko Ota graduated from the Rochester Institute of Technology and lives in Maryland. She has worked as an animator and a lab assistant but is happiest drawing creatures and inventing worlds. She likes strong tea, the smell of new tyres, and polydactyl cats (cats with extra toes!). She doesn't have any pets, but she has seven houseplants named Blue, Wolf, Charlene, Charlie, Roberto, Steven, and Doris.

Der-shing Helmer graduated with a degree in Biology from UC Berkeley, where she played with snakes and lizards all summer long. She is working towards becoming a biology teacher. When she is not coaching kids, she likes to create art, especially comics. Her best friends are her two pet geckoes (Smeg and Jerry), her king snake (Clarice), and the chinchilla that lives next door.

AMY BY TINTIN

START READING FROM THE OTHER SIDE OF THE BOOK!

This page would be the first page of a manga from Japan. This is because written Japanese is read from the right side of the page to the left side of the page.

English is read from left to right, so this is the last page of this Manga Maths Mystery. If you read the end of the book first, you'll spoil the mystery! Turn the book over so you can start on the first page. Then find the clues to the mystery with Sam, Joy, Amy, and Adam!

MANGA MATHS MYSTERIES

JOIN THE KIDS FROM THE KUNG FU SCHOOL IN SOLVING ALL THE MANGA MATHS MYSTERIES!

MANGA MATHS MYSTERIES